HOW DO YOU MAKE A SKELETON LAUGH?

HALLOWEEN RIDDLES, PUZZLES, AND GAMES

BY JIM GALLAGHER & HELENE HOVANEC

A TRUMPET CLUB ORIGINAL BOOK

12 11 10 9 8 7 6 5 4 3 2 1   7 8 9/9 0 12/0

Printed in the U.S.A.

First Scholastic printing, October 1997

A-MAZE #1

Make a path through this maze and stop at each house just one time.

START

HA! HA!

Fill in the numbered spaces below with the letters indicated and answer this riddle:

HOW DO YOU MAKE A SKELETON LAUGH?

B = 15
C = 3
E = 6, 18
F = 10
I = 2, 7
K = 4
L = 5
N = 12, 13, 17
O = 16
S = 9
T = 1, 8
U = 11
Y = 14

___ ___ ___ ___ ___ ___   ___ ___ ___
1   2   3   4   5   6   7   8   9

___ ___ ___ ___ ___   ___ ___ ___ ___
10 11 12 13 14   15 16 17 18

 4

SOME DIFFERENCE #1

Find five differences between these two "broom-mates."

WILDLIFE

Fill in the blank space on each line with a letter that will spell the name of a wild animal. Then read down the column to find the answer to this riddle:

WHAT IS DRACULA'S FAVORITE ANIMAL?

TI _ ER

L _ ON

ZEB _ A

C _ MEL

_ OX

WOL _

AP _

MAKING CONNECTIONS #1

Connect the dots from 1 to 50 to find a Halloween scene.

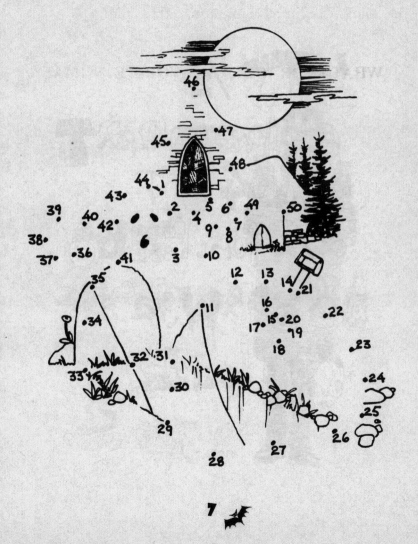

LET'S PARTY!

Add the pictures and words together to read an "invitation."

SIGN OF THE TIMES

Color each space that has a dark circle (•) and you'll find a seasonal sign.

COLOR-FULL

There are ten color words hidden below. Cross off one or two colors in each line. After you find all of them, read the UNUSED letters from left to right and top to bottom to find the two most popular colors on October 31.

G	R	A	Y	R	E	D
B	V	I	O	L	E	T
G	R	E	E	N	L	A
C	A	Q	U	A	K	A
M	A	G	E	N	T	A
N	B	R	O	W	N	D
Y	E	L	L	O	W	O
R	W	H	I	T	E	A
N	G	P	I	N	K	E

ORANGE AID

Now that you know the main Halloween colors, place each orange thing into the grid. There's just one spot for each item. (Hint: Place the only ten-letter word in the only ten-letter space.)

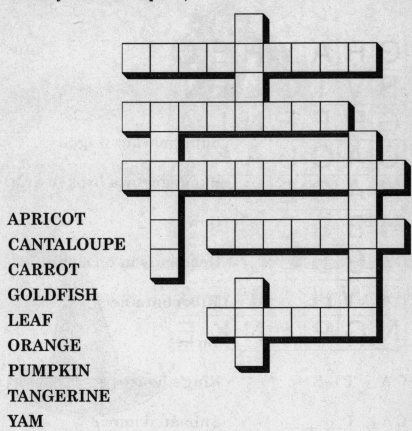

APRICOT
CANTALOUPE
CARROT
GOLDFISH
LEAF
ORANGE
PUMPKIN
TANGERINE
YAM

PURR-FECTION

Here are a bunch of Halloween cats that can be changed to other things. Just add the right letters to each blank space and make words that answer the clues.

C A _ T   Supermarket wagon

C A _ T   Bandage for a broken arm

C A T _ _ _   Cows

C A _ T _ _ _   Head person on a ship

C A _ T _ _   Milk container

C _ A T   Jacket

C A _ T L E   King's house

C A _ T _ _ _   Animated movie

SPELLING LINES #1

After you recognize each thing in the top boxes, write
the first letter of its name in the box at the other end of
the line. Then read the letters across to spell the name
of a "frequent flyer."

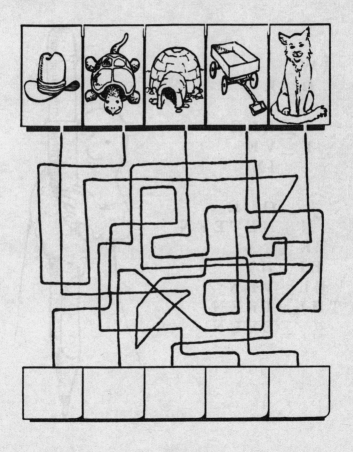

NEW MATH

Fill in the blank space on each line to make a number word. Then read down the column to answer this riddle:

HOW DOES A MONSTER COUNT TO 33?

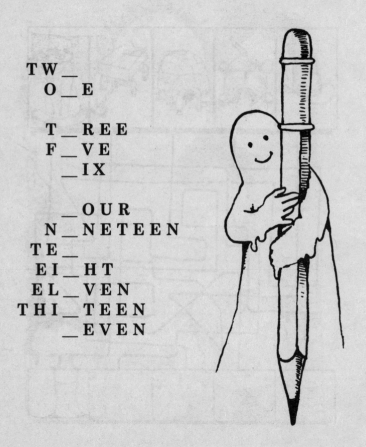

T W _ _
  O _ E

  T _ R E E
  F _ V E
  _ I X

  _ O U R
  N _ N E T E E N
T E _
 E I _ H T
 E L _ V E N
T H I _ T E E N
 _ E V E N

FREAKY FOLKS

Draw facial features on these folks to make them as frightening as possible.

CHANGELINGS

Follow the directions on each line and you'll change
the first word you write into something completely
different. Hint: Write very neatly.

1. Write the name of the holiday
celebrated on October 31. _____

2. Change the eighth letter to an "R." _____

3. Replace the fourth, fifth, and sixth
letters with "ANT." _____

4. Place the letters "CKO" after
the first "A." _____

5. Change the "H" to a "J." _____

6. Place a hyphen (-) after the
fourth letter. _____

7. Place an apostrophe after the
fifth letter. _____

8. Place another hyphen (-) after the
apostrophe. _____

MISSING PIECE

These kids want to go trick-or-treating. But they can't get moving until they find the missing piece to the car. Which piece was removed from the scene?

WISECRACKS

Look at the words on the opposite page and cross off the groups described below. When you're finished, read the remaining words from left to right and top to bottom to find a riddle and its answer.

1. Cross off three coins.

2. Cross off four relatives.

3. Cross off five European cities.

4. Cross off five fruits.

5. Cross off four face parts.

6. Cross off four words that rhyme with SLEEP.

7. Cross off four things to wear on your feet.

WHAT   PARIS   AUNT   QUARTERS   IS

PLUMS   CREEP   THE   NOSE   SANDALS

COUSIN   NICKELS   SOCKS   MOUTH   EYES

BEST   SHEEP   PENNIES   WAY   MADRID

LEMONS   TO   SNEAKERS.

TALK   LOAFERS

CHEEKS   TO   BANANAS   A

MUNICH   VAMPIRE

BEEP   PEACHES   BY   STEPMOTHER

LONG   ROME

UNCLE   DEEP   VIENNA   DISTANCE   PEARS

CUTE COUPLE

One couple on this page is exactly the same as one couple on the opposite page. Can you find them?

ESCAPE ARTISTS

Uh-oh! The creature keeper got loose and chewed off pieces of some Halloween folks. You can put these awful people back together by placing one of the two-letter words from the right column into each empty space in the left column.

W _ _ C H   AM

M _ _ S T E R   AN

S K E L E _ _ N   GO

G _ _ S T   HO

_ _ R E W O L F   IT

V _ _ P I R E   MY

C _ _ N I B A L   ON

_ _ B L I N   TO

M U M _ _   WE

A-MAZE #2

Look at this three-dimensional maze and walk the boy through the hedges to the exit.

SLIGHT CHANGE

Change the starred letters in each word to find two riddles and answers below.

WHIT   MIND   IF   BILL   GATE   GOES
 *   *   *   *   *   *

I   MOISTER   BIKE?
*   *   *

I   DOABLELEADER
*   *   *

WAY   ATE   GRANTS   DICE
 *   *   *   *

GO   WAVE   GROUND?
*   *   *

THEM   IRE   I   SON   IF   FIN.
  *   *   *   *   *   *

SCARY STUFF

There's one Halloween word hidden in this picture.
How fast can you find it?

ALPHA-BETICS

Put each word into the grid in alphabetical order. Then read down one of the columns to find a Halloween event.

HEELS

DESKS

EATER

PURSE

GAMES

BACON

STYLE

NEARS

FRUIT

RATES

CLOWN

MAPLE

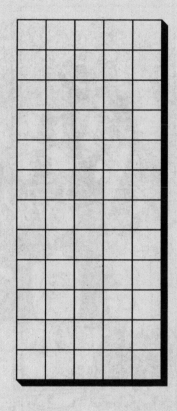

SOME DIFFERENCE #2

Find five differences between these two pirates.

PLEASE BE SEATED

The letters in both words (or phrases) on each line are the same except for one extra letter. Put that extra letter in the blank space. Then read DOWN to answer this riddle:

WHERE DOES A GHOST WANT TO SIT WHEN HE GOES TO THE THEATER?

CHAIR	__	CHAR
SWING	__	WIGS
SADDLE	__	DEALS
CAR SEAT	__	CARATS
HASSOCK	__	SHOCKS
PAD	__	PA
COUCH	__	OUCH
THRONE	__	NORTH
DIVAN	__	AVID
STOOL	__	SOLO
SEAT	__	SAT
RECLINER	__	RECLINE

STORY LINE

Number the boxes from 1 to 6 to make a story without words.

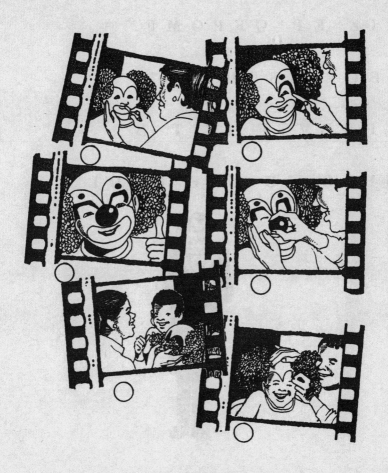

OUTCAST

Find a riddle and its answer by changing each letter to the one that comes just before it in the alphabet.

X I Z   E P   Q F P Q M F

I B U F   E S B D V M B?

C F D B V T F   I F ' T   B

Q B J O   J O   U I F   O F D L.

SPELLING LINES #2

After you recognize each thing in the top boxes, write the first letter of its name in the box at the other end of the line. Then read the letters across to spell the name of a type of "yard." (Hint: Think scary!)

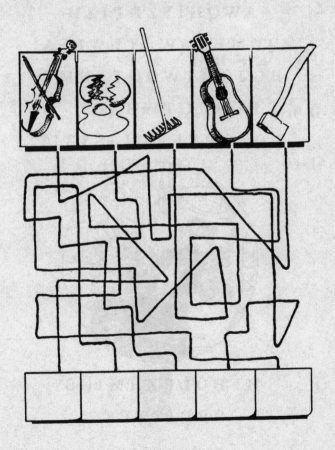

BRACE YOURSELF

Circle every second letter (or symbol). Read only the circled letters from left to right and top to bottom to find a riddle and its answer.

A W Q H I Y Z D P I X D

Q D M R N A W C T U W L S A

B G J O M T W O Q T P H M E

B O S R G T W H X O * -

L D Z O P N K T Q I J S Y T ! ?

H F B O L R Z H M I G S

C B D I Z T P E .

HIDDEN WORDS

There are five Halloween words hidden in this picture.
Can you find each one?

SWEET TREAT

A riddle and its answer are hidden here. To find them, do the following:

- Answer each clue and write the word in the numbered spaces.
- Put the letters into the same numbered spaces on the opposite page.

Tell your teacher this riddle!

The opposite of slow

$\overline{}\ \overline{}\ \overline{}\ \overline{}$
34 16 24 4

Female parent

$\overline{}\ \overline{}\ \overline{}\ \overline{}\ \overline{}\ \overline{}$
12 35 27 2 41 20

The opposite of even

$\overline{}\ \overline{}\ \overline{}$
13 5 28

The color of cherries

$\overline{}\ \overline{}\ \overline{}$
26 29 37

Unable to hear

$\overline{}\ \overline{}\ \overline{}\ \overline{}$
21 15 3 18

A toy that flies

$\overline{}\ \overline{}\ \overline{}\ \overline{}$
40 31 17 25

Rescue (someone) from danger

    __ __ __ __
    23 39 30 11

Building material for furniture

    __ __ __ __
    1 6 19 10

Walking sticks

    __ __ __ __ __
    38 9 14 7 33

The opposite of win

    __ __ __ __
    32 36 8 22

__ __ __ __   __ __ __ __   __
1 2 3 4   5 6 7 8   9

__ __ __ __ __   __ __ __
10 11 12 13 14   15 16 17

__ __ __   __ __ __ __ __ __ __?
18 19 20   21 22 23 24 25 26 27

__ __ __ __ __   __   __ __ __ __ ,
28 29 30 31 32   33   34 35 36 37

__ __ __ __ .
38 39 40 41

RIDDLE READ

A riddle and its answer are written here. The words are in the correct order, but the spacing is wrong. Can you read it?

WHA TD

OBI RDSS

AY ON

HAL LOWE

EN? TWI

CKO RT

WE ET

LOST AND FOUND

Look at the ten pictures to the right of the pencil on the opposite page. Each one is hidden somewhere in this big picture. Can you find and circle each one?

HOUSEWORK

In the grid on the next page, find and circle each of the twelve areas of a house listed below. Look forward, backward, up, down, and diagonally. **KITCHEN** is circled to start you off. When you've circled all the words, write the **UNUSED** letters from the grid in the blank spaces at the bottom of the opposite page. Go in order from left to right and top to bottom,. and you'll answer this riddle:

WHAT ROOM DOES A ZOMBIE STAY OUT OF?

ATTIC
BASEMENT
BATH
DEN
GARAGE
GYM
KITCHEN
LOFT
NURSERY
PANTRY
PARLOR
STUDY

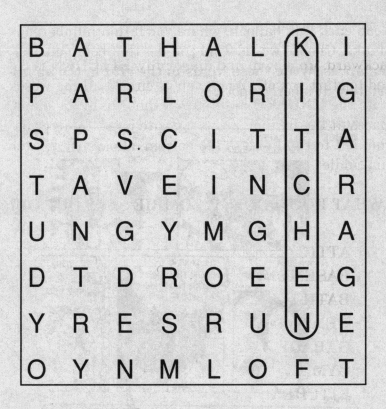

B	A	T	H	A	L	K	I
P	A	R	L	O	R	I	G
S	P	S	C	I	T	T	A
T	A	V	E	I	N	C	R
U	N	G	Y	M	G	H	A
D	T	D	R	O	E	E	G
Y	R	E	S	R	U	N	E
O	Y	N	M	L	O	F	T

RIDDLE ANSWER:

_ _ _ _ _ _ _ _ _ _ _

CROSSTALK

Read each talk balloon, where you'll find numbered blanks. Choose words from the list that complete the sentences. Write those words in the grid in the appropriately numbered spots.

ACROSS CLUES

I'LL CARRY A ___1___ BAG TO HOLD THE GOODIES.

IF WE GET A ___5___ WE WON'T HAVE TO ___6___ A TRICK!

I HOPE OUR ___7___ HAND OUT LOTS OF ___9___.

I'LL TAKE A ___11___ FROM THE LINEN CLOSET AND BE A GHOST.

YOU ___12___ THE BELL.

DOWN CLUES

ON ___2___ NIGHT WE MARCH IN A ___6___.

SOME OF THE KIDS WEAR ___4___ COSTUMES.

THERE'S AN UGLY ___8___!

DOWN CLUES

THE ___3___ WILL START AT 7 O'CLOCK.

COOL!

I'LL OPEN THE ___10___ FOR THE GUESTS.

WORD LIST:

CANDY
DOOR
HALLOWEEN
NEIGHBORS
PARADE
PARTY
PLAY
RING
SCARY
SHEET
SHOPPING
TREAT
WITCH

SPOOKY SCRAMBLERS

Unscramble the letters of each word below to find two riddles and their answers.

HNEW   RESAMPIV   OG   OT   AJLI   WEHER

OD   HEYT   ASTY?

NI   BDOLO   CLESL.

HWTA   HGTOS   PHLES   NIW   AMGES?

HTE   ATME   SIRPTI.

PLAYMATES?

Match each Halloween character on the left with a related item on the right.

BATTING PRACTICE

Each of these BAT words will fit into one spot in the grid on the next page. Can you place each one without going BATTY?

FIVE LETTERS
BATON

SIX LETTERS
COMBAT

SEVEN LETTERS
ACROBAT   BATTERY
BATBOYS   SABBATH

EIGHT LETTERS
BATHROBE

NINE LETTERS
INCUBATOR

TEN LETTERS
BATTLESHIP

TWELVE LETTERS
BATTLEGROUND

 44

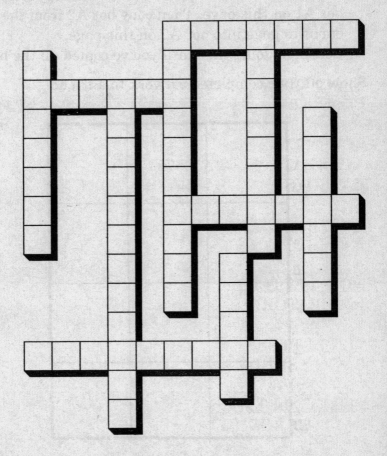

DRAW IT!

The boxes on the opposite page will make a Halloween picture if you follow these directions:

Find box A1 on the opposite page and copy it into box A1 on this page. Then copy box A2 from the opposite page into box A2 on this page.
Continue doing this until you've copied all the boxes.

Show off your completed artwork to a friend!

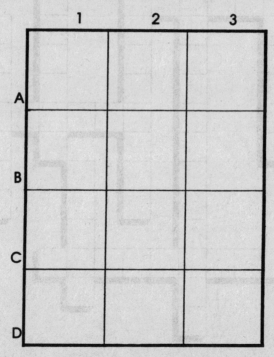

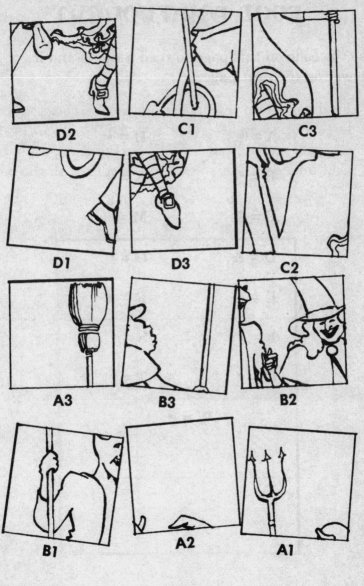

D2

C1

C3

D1

D3

C2

A3

B3

B2

B1

A2

A1

FOOD FOR THOUGHT

Use the code on this page to read a riddle and its answer on the next page.

A = @	H = •
B = ¶	K = #
C = $	M = %
D = &	O = *
E = Δ	R =
F = +	S = √
G = ¤	T = ‡
W = ¢	

¢ • @ ‡   & *

¤ • * √ ‡ √

Δ @ ‡   + *

¶ Δ @ # + @ √ ‡ ?

√ $ Δ @ %

* +   ¢ • Δ @ ‡ .

49

BOXED OUT

Each small picture on the opposite page is part of the large picture on this page. Can you locate each one by number and letter?

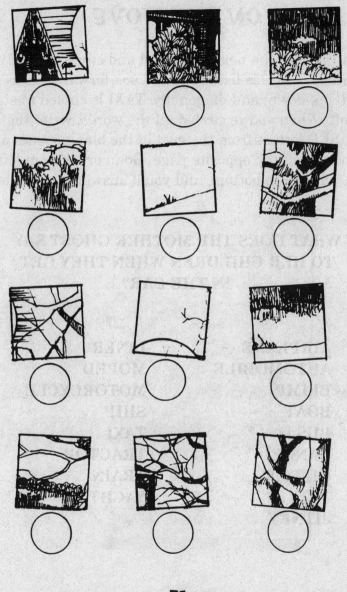

ON THE MOVE

In the grid on the next page, find and circle each of the seventeen vehicles listed below. Look forward, backward, up, down, and diagonally. TAXI is circled to start you off. When you've circled all the words, write the UNUSED letters from the grid in the blank spaces at the bottom of the opposite page. Go in order from left to right and top to bottom, and you'll answer this riddle:

**WHAT DOES THE MOTHER GHOST SAY
TO HER CHILDREN WHEN THEY GET
IN THE CAR?**

AIRPLANE	**LINER**
AUTOMOBILE	**MOPED**
BLIMP	**MOTORCYCLE**
BOAT	**SHIP**
BUS	**TAXI**
CANOE	**TRACTOR**
GLIDER	**TRAIN**
JET	**YACHT**
JITNEY	

M	O	P	E	D	F	B	U	S	A
A	O	R	E	N	I	L	N	H	U
J	E	T	(T	A	X	I)	S	I	T
I	G	B	O	T	A	M	E	P	O
T	L	O	N	R	Y	P	O	U	M
N	I	A	T	R	C	S	H	E	O
E	D	T	H	C	A	Y	E	T	B
Y	E	B	E	O	N	A	C	E	I
T	R	A	C	T	O	R	L	L	L
T	S	A	I	R	P	L	A	N	E

RIDDLE ANSWER:

_ _ _ _ _ _ _ _ _ _

_ _ _ _ _ _ _ _ _

MAKING CONNECTIONS #2

Connect the dots from 1 to 60 to find out what the horse's rider will wear to the costume party.

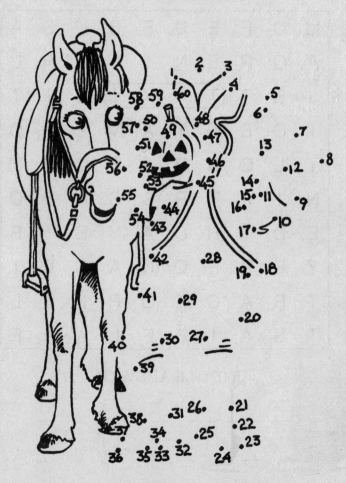

REAL JUNK FOOD

Don't eat any of these foods ... until you change the starred letters to find the real foods.

ROOKIES
*

DANDY   BORN
*   *

JOLLY   DEANS
    *   *

ACE   DREAM
*   *

RAISING
            *

GUTS
*

POISON APPLES

Go through the maze and collect each poison apple WITHOUT RETRACING YOUR PATH. Be careful! It's tricky!

ANSWERS

A-MAZE #1   page 3

HA! HA!   page 4

Tickle its funny bone.

SOME DIFFERENCE #1
page 5

WILDLIFE   page 6

TIGER
LION
ZEBRA
CAMEL
FOX
WOLF
APE

Giraffe

MAKING
CONNECTIONS #1   page 7

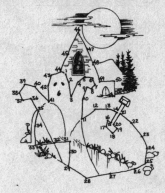

LET'S PARTY!   page 8

*Let's have a Halloween party.
We'll bob for apples and have
fun. Please bring soda and
candy and wear a costume.
See you later alligator.*

SIGN OF THE TIMES
page 9

COLOR-FULL   page 10

Black and orange

ORANGE AID   page 11

PURR-FECTION   page 12

CART
CAST
CATTLE
CAPTAIN
CARTON
COAT
CASTLE
CARTOON

SPELLING LINES #1
page 13

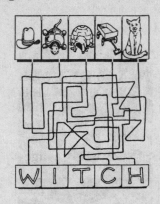

NEW MATH   page 14

TWO
  ONE

  THREE
  FIVE
    SIX

  FOUR
  NINETEEN
TEN
  EIGHT
  ELEVEN
THIRTEEN
    SEVEN

On his fingers

CHANGELINGS page 16

1. H A L L O W E E N
2. H A L L O W E R N
3. H A L A N T E R N
4. H A C K O L A N T E R N
5. J A C K O L A N T E R N
6. J A C K - O L A N T E R N
7. J A C K - O' L A N T E R N
8. J A C K - O' - L A N T E R N

MISSING PIECE page 17

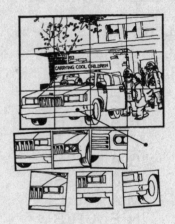

WISECRACKS pages 18-19

1. Quarters, nickels, pennies
2. Aunt, cousin, stepmother, uncle
3. Paris, Madrid, Munich, Rome, Vienna
4. Plums, lemons, bananas, peaches, pears
5. Nose, mouth, eyes, cheeks
6. Creep, sheep, beep, deep
7. Sandals, socks, sneakers, loafers

What is the best way to talk to a vampire?
By long distance.

CUTE COUPLE
pages 20-21

ESCAPE ARTISTS page 22

<u>WI</u>TCH
<u>MO</u>NSTER
SKELE<u>TO</u>N
G<u>H</u>OST
<u>WE</u>REWOLF
<u>VA</u>MPIRE
CA<u>N</u>NIBAL
<u>GO</u>BLIN
MUM<u>MY</u>

SCARY STUFF page 25

A-MAZE #2 page 23

SLIGHT CHANGE page 24

*What kind of ball game
does a monster like?
A doubleheader.
Why are giants nice to
have around?
They are a ton of fun.*

ALPHA-BETICS page 26

B	A	C	O	N
C	L	O	W	N
D	E	S	K	S
E	A	T	E	R
F	R	U	I	T
G	A	M	E	S
H	E	E	L	S
M	A	P	L	E
N	E	A	R	S
P	U	R	S	E
R	A	T	E	S
S	T	Y	L	E

Costume party

SOME DIFFERENCE #2
page 27

PLEASE BE SEATED
page 28

CHAIR	I	CHAR
SWING	N	WIGS
SADDLE	D	DEALS
CAR SEAT	E	CARATS
HASSOCK	A	SHOCKS
PAD	D	PA
COUCH	C	OUCH
THRONE	E	NORTH
DIVAN	N	AVID
STOOL	T	SOLO
SEAT	E	SAT
RECLINER	R	RECLINE

In dead center

STORY LINE
page 29

OUTCAST   page 30

Why do people hate Dracula?
Because he's a pain
in the neck.

SPELLING LINES #2
page 31

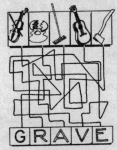

BRACE YOURSELF
page 32

Why did Dracula go
to the orthodontist?
For his bite.

HIDDEN WORDS
page 33

SWEET TREAT
pages 34-35

Fast
Mother
Odd
Red
Deaf
Kite
Save
Wood
Canes
Lose

*What does a demon
eat for dessert?*
Devil's food cake.

RIDDLE READ   page 36

*What do birds say on
Halloween?*
Twick or tweet.

LOST AND FOUND
pages 36-37

HOUSEWORK   pages 38-39

A living room

CROSSTALK   pages 40-41

SPOOKY SCRAMBLERS
page 42

*When vampires go to jail
where do they stay?
In blood cells.*

*What ghost helps win games?
The team spirit.*

PLAYMATES? page 43

DRAW IT! pages 46-47

FOOD FOR THOUGHT
pages 48-49

What do ghosts eat for breakfast?
Scream of wheat.

BATTING PRACTICE
pages 44-45

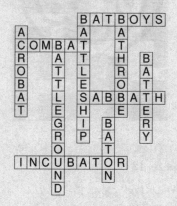

BOXED OUT   pages 50-51

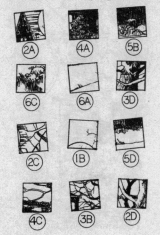

ON THE MOVE
pages 52-53

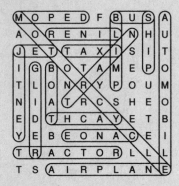

Fasten your sheet belts.

MAKING
CONNECTIONS #2
page 54

REAL JUNK FOOD
page 55

Cookies
Candy corn
Jelly beans
Ice cream
Raisins
Nuts

POISON APPLES   page 56